THE
FOLLETT
BEGINNING-TO-READ
SERIES

Compiled by Sally Clithero

Illustrated by
Erik Blegvad

Beginning-To-Read POETRY

Selected from Original Sources

FOLLETT PUBLISHING COMPANY

Chicago  New York

ACKNOWLEDGMENTS

The compiler and publisher wish to express their appreciation to the following publishers and persons for permission to reproduce the following poems:

"A Little Frog" by Alice Wilkins. Copyright 1932 by The John Day Company, Inc. Reprinted from *The Golden Flute* by Alice H. Hubbard and Adeline Babbitt by permission of the publisher.

"Spring Rain," from *Around and About* by Marchette Chute, copyright 1941. Published 1957 by E. P. Dutton & Co., Inc. and reprinted with their permission.

"Mud" by Polly Chase Boyden, from *Child Life Magazine* copyright 1930, 1958, Rand McNally. Reprinted by permission of Barbara Boyden Jordan.

"The Caterpillar" from *Sing-Song* by Christina Rossetti. Copyright 1924 by The Macmillan Company and reprinted by their permission.

"Only My Opinion" from *Goose Grass Rhymes* by Monica Shannon. Copyright 1930 by Doubleday & Company, Inc. Reprinted by permission of the publisher.

"The Little Elf" by John Kendrick Bangs, from *St. Nicholas Magazine,* September, 1893, copyright, The Century Company. Reprinted by courtesy of Appleton-Century-Crofts.

"Jump or Jiggle" by Evelyn Beyer, from *Another Here and Now Story Book* by Lucy Sprague Mitchell. Copyright, 1937, by E. P. Dutton & Co., Inc. Renewal, © 1967 by Lucy Sprague Mitchell. Reprinted by permission of the publishers.

"Choosing Shoes" by ffrida Wolfe, from *The Very Thing,* published by Sidgewick & Jackson, Ltd. and used with their permission.

"Skyscrapers" from *The Pointed People* by Rachel Field. Copyright 1924, 1930 by The Macmillan Company. Reprinted by permission of the publishers.

"The Park" from *I Live in a City* by James S. Tippett. Copyright 1927 Harper & Brothers. Reprinted by permission of Harper & Row, Publishers, Inc. and Mrs. Martha K. Tippett.

"Make-Believe House" from the book *Me* by Inez Hogan. Copyright 1954, by Inez Hogan. Reprinted by permission of E. P. Dutton & Co., Inc.

"Whistles" from *Here, There and Everywhere* by Dorothy Aldis. Copyright 1927, 1928 by Dorothy Aldis. Reprinted by permission of G. P. Putnam's Sons.

"Mrs. Peck-Pigeon" from *Poems for Children* by Eleanor Farjeon. Copyright 1933, 1961 by Eleanor Farjeon. Reprinted by permission of J. B. Lippincott Company and Harold Ober Associates, Inc.

"The Little Turtle" from *Collected Poems* by Vachel Lindsay. Copyright 1920 by The Macmillan Company. Renewed 1948 by Elizabeth C. Lindsay. Reprinted by permission of The Macmillan Company.

"Mice" from *Fifty-One New Nursery Rhymes* by Rose Fyleman. Copyright 1932 by Doubleday & Company, Inc. Reprinted by permission of the publishers and The Society of Authors for the Rose Fyleman Estate.

"First Snow" from *A Pocketful of Rhymes* by Marie Louise Allen. Copyright 1939 Harper & Brothers and used by permission of Harper & Row, Publishers.

"Snow" from *Everything and Anything* by Dorothy Aldis. Copyright 1925, 1927 by Dorothy Aldis. Reprinted by permission of G. P. Putnam's Sons.

"Up in the Air" from *I Go A-Traveling* by James S. Tippett. Copyright 1929 Harper & Brothers and used by permission of Harper & Row, Publishers.

"The Butterfly" by Clinton Scollard, from *Child Life Magazine,* copyright 1924, 1952 by Rand McNally & Co. and used with their permission.

"Holding Hands" by Lenore M. Link, from *St. Nicholas Magazine,* June, 1936. Used by permission.

"Shore" from *Menagerie* by Mary Britton Miller. Published by The Macmillan Company, 1928. Reprinted by permission of the author.

"Firefly" from *Under the Tree* by Elizabeth Madox Roberts. Copyright 1922 by B. W. Huebsch, Inc., 1950 by Ivor S. Roberts. Reprinted by permission of The Viking Press, Inc.

 Manufactured in the United States of America. Published simultaneously in Canada by The Ryerson Press, Toronto.

Library of Congress Catalog Card Number: 67-21167 First Printing T/L/A 7150

A LIST OF THE POEMS

A Little Frog	Back Cover
Spring Rain	6
Mud	7
The Caterpillar	8
Only My Opinion	9
The Little Elf	10
Jump or Jiggle	11
Choosing Shoes	12
Skyscrapers	14
The Park	15
Make-Believe House	16
Whistles	17
Mrs. Peck-Pigeon	18
The Little Turtle	19
The Squirrel	20
Mice	21
First Snow	22
Snow	23
Up in the Air	24
The Butterfly	25
Holding Hands	26
Shore	27
Firefly	28
Bed in Summer	29
School is Over	30

Spring Rain

The storm came up so very quick
  It couldn't have been quicker.
I should have brought my hat along,
  I should have brought my slicker.

My hair is wet, my feet are wet,
  I couldn't be much wetter.
I fell into a river once,
  But this is even better.

Marchette Chute

Mud

Mud is very nice to feel
All squishy – squash between the toes!
I'd rather wade in wiggly mud
Than smell a yellow rose.

Nobody else but the rosebush knows
How nice mud feels
Between the toes.

Polly Chase Boyden

The Caterpillar

Brown and furry
Caterpillar in a hurry;
Take your walk
To the shady leaf, or stalk.

May no toad spy you,
May the little birds pass by you;
Spin and die,
To live again a butterfly.

Christina Rossetti

Only My Opinion

Is a caterpillar ticklish?
  Well, it's always my belief
That he giggles, as he wiggles
  Across a hairy leaf.

Monica Shannon

The Little Elf

I met a little Elf-man once,
  Down where the lilies blow.
I asked him why he was so small,
  And why he didn't grow.

He slightly frowned, and with his eye
  He looked me through and through.
"I'm quite as big for me," said he,
  "As you are big for you."

John Kendrick Bangs

Jump or Jiggle

Frogs jump
Caterpillars hump

Worms wiggle
Bugs jiggle

Rabbits hop
Horses clop

Snakes slide
Sea gulls glide

Mice creep
Deer leap

Puppies bounce
Kittens pounce

Lions stalk –
But –
I walk!

Evelyn Beyer

Choosing Shoes

New shoes, new shoes,
Red and pink and blue shoes.
Tell me, what would *you* choose,
If they'd let us buy?

Buckle shoes, bow shoes,
Pretty pointy-toe shoes,
Strappy, cappy low shoes;
Let's have some to try.

Bright shoes, white shoes,
  Dandy-dance-by-night shoes,
Perhaps-a-little-tight shoes,
  Like some? So would I.

But

Flat shoes, fat shoes,
  Stump-along-like-that shoes,
Wipe-them-on-the-mat shoes,
  That's the sort they'll buy.

ffrida Wolfe

Skyscrapers

Do skyscrapers ever grow tired
Of holding themselves up high?
Do they ever shiver on frosty nights
With their tops against the sky?
Do they feel lonely sometimes
Because they have grown so tall?
Do they ever wish they could lie right down
And never get up at all?

Rachel Field

The Park

I'm glad that I
   Live near a park

For in the winter
   After dark

The park lights shine
   As bright and still

As dandelions
   On a hill.

James S. Tippett

Make-Believe House

I put a blanket
Over a chair.
Then it's my house
I live there.

Now I'm an Indian,
Hunting for deer.
This is my tent—
I live here.

Now I'm a lion.
This is my den.
Better stay out—
I—eat—Men!

Inez Hogan

Whistles

I want to learn to whistle.
I've always wanted to.
I fix my mouth to do it but
The whistle won't come through.

I think perhaps it's stuck, and so
I try it once again.
Can people swallow whistles?
Where is my whistle then?

Dorothy Aldis

Mrs. Peck-Pigeon

Mrs. Peck-Pigeon
Is picking for bread,
Bob-bob-bob
Goes her little round head.
Tame as a pussy-cat
In the street,
Step-step-step
Go her little red feet.
With her little red feet
And her little round head,
Mrs. Peck-Pigeon
Goes picking for bread.

Eleanor Farjeon

The Little Turtle

There was a little turtle.
He lived in a box.
He swam in a puddle.
He climbed on the rocks.

He snapped at a mosquito.
He snapped at a flea.
He snapped at a minnow.
And he snapped at me.

He caught the mosquito.
He caught the flea.
He caught the minnow.
But he didn't catch me.

Vachel Lindsay

The Squirrel

Whisky, frisky,
Hippity hop,
Up he goes
To the tree top!

Whirly, twirly,
Round and round,
Down he scampers
To the ground.

Furly, curly
What a tail!
Tall as a feather
Broad as a sail!

Where's his supper?
In the shell,
Snappity, crackity,
Out it fell.

Unknown

Mice

I think mice
Are rather nice.

Their tails are long,
Their faces small,
They haven't any
Chins at all.
Their ears are pink,
Their teeth are white,
They run about
The house at night.
They nibble things
They shouldn't touch
And no one seems
To like them much.

But *I* think mice
Are nice.

Rose Fyleman

First Snow

Snow makes whiteness where it falls.
The bushes look like popcorn-balls.
And places where I always play,
Look like somewhere else today.

Marie Louise Allen

Snow

The fenceposts wear marshmallow hats
On a snowy day;
Bushes in their nightgowns
Are kneeling down to pray—
And all the trees have silver skirts
And want to dance away.

Dorothy Aldis

Up in the Air

Zooming across the sky
Like a great bird you fly,
    Airplane,
    Silvery white
    In the light.

Turning and twisting in air,
When shall I ever be there,
    Airplane,
    Piloting you
    Far in the blue?

James S. Tippett

The Butterfly

Up and down the air you float
Like a little fairy boat;
I should like to sail the sky,
Gliding like a butterfly!

Clinton Scollard

Holding Hands

Elephants walking
Along the trails

Are holding hands
By holding tails.

Trunks and tails
Are handy things

When elephants walk
In Circus rings.

Elephants work
And elephants play

And elephants walk
And feel so gay.

And when they walk –
It never fails.

They're holding hands
By holding tails.

Lenore M. Link

Shore

Play on the seashore
And gather up shells,
Kneel in the damp sands
Digging wells.

Run on the rocks
Where the seaweed slips,
Watch the waves
And the beautiful ships.

Mary Britton Miller

Firefly

A little light is going by,
Is going up to see the sky
A little light with wings.

I never could have thought of it,
To have a little bug all lit
And made to go on wings.

Elizabeth Madox Roberts

Bed in Summer

In winter I get up at night
And dress by yellow candlelight.
In summer, quite the other way,
I have to go to bed by day.

I have to go to bed and see
The birds still hopping on the tree,
Or hear the grown-up people's feet
Still going past me in the street.

And does it not seem hard to you,
When all the sky is clear and blue,
And I should like so much to play,
To have to go to bed by day?

Robert Louis Stevenson

School is Over

School is over,
  Oh, what fun!
Lessons finished,
  Play begun.
Who'll run fastest,
  You or I?
Who'll laugh loudest?
  Let us try.

Kate Greenaway

A poem is a happy thing
That makes you think or feel or sing.
For in its special, secret way
It makes things golden that were gray.
And if you learn when you are small
To heed the magic in its call,
It's sure to spread your soul apart
And leave a mark upon your heart.

This book is a perfect introduction to poetry for the young child. A compilation of twenty-five previously published favorites, selected from original sources, it is a book third graders can read themselves and enjoy.

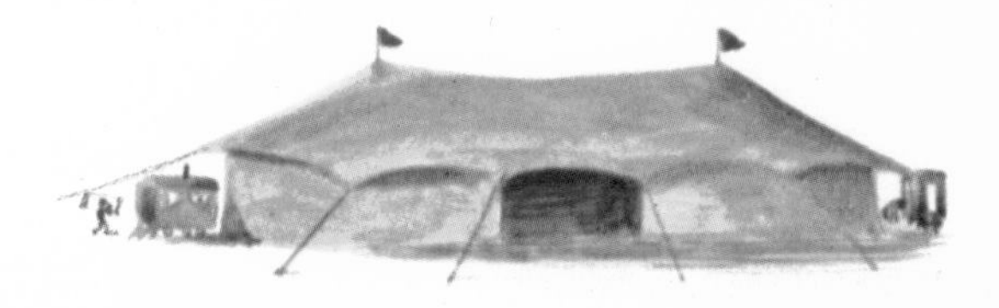

Erik Blegvad was born in Copenhagen, Denmark, where his childhood was spent. He has illustrated articles and stories for various periodicals, in addition to numerous books. After spending fifteen years in the United States, he now lives in London with his American wife and two sons.

Before her marriage, **Sally Clithero** taught for two years in a one-room schoolhouse and three years in the Oak Park Lincoln Elementary School in Illinois. For the past several years she has been teaching in the primary department of the Sterling, Illinois schools.